D1296042

© 2002 Algrove Publishing Limited
ALL RIGHTS RESERVED.
No part of this book may be reproduced in any form, including photocopying, without permission in writing from the publishers, except by a reviewer who may quote brief passages in a magazine or newspaper or on radio or television.

Algrove Publishing Limited
1090 Morrison Drive
Ottawa, Ontario
Canada K2H 1C2

National Library of Canada Cataloguing in Publication Data

Dudeney, Henry Ernest, 1857-1930
    Classic puzzles and how to solve them / Henry Ernest Dudeney.

(Classic reprint series)
Reprint of: Modern puzzles and how to solve them. London : C.A.
    Pearson, 1926.
ISBN 1-894572-58-0

    1. Puzzles. I. Title. II. Title: Modern puzzles and how to solve
them. III. Series: Classic reprint series (Ottawa, Ont.)

GV1493.D83 2002   793.73   C2002-904388-3

Printed in Canada
#11002

PUBLISHER'S NOTE

The puzzles in this book were selected from *Modern Puzzles and How To Solve Them,* originally published in 1926. Some have been altered by changing the currency to dollars and cents from pounds, shillings and pence. Otherwise, they remain as in the original.

Leonard G. Lee, Publisher
Ottawa
September, 2002

ARITHMETICAL AND ALGEBRAICAL PROBLEMS

MONEY PROBLEMS

~1~
DOLLARS AND CENTS

An American correspondent tells me that a man went into a store and spent one-half of the money that was in his pocket. When he came out he found that he had just as many cents as he had dollars when he went in and half as many dollars as he had cents when he went in. How much money did he have on him when he entered?

~2~
UNREWARDED LABOUR

A man persuaded Weary Willie, with some difficulty, to try to work on a job for thirty days at 24 dollars a day, on the condition that he would forfeit 30 dollars a day for every day that he idled. At the end of the month neither owed the other anything, which entirely convinced Willie of the folly of labour. Now, can you tell just how many days' work he put in, and on how many days he idled?

~3~
THE PERPLEXED BANKER

A man went into a bank with a thousand silver dollars and ten bags. He said, "Place this money, please, in the bags in such a way that if I call and ask for a certain number of silver dollars you can hand me over one or more bags, giving me the exact amount called for without opening any of the bags." How was it to be done? We are, of course, only concerned with a single application, but he may ask for any exact number of dollars from $1 to $1000.

~4~
SAWING LOGS

"Your charge," said Mr. Grigsby, "was thirty dollars for sawing up three cords of wood made up of logs three feet long, each log to be cut into pieces one foot in length."

"That is so," the man replied.

"Well, here are four cords of logs, all of the same thickness as before, only they are in six-feet lengths, instead of three feet. What will your charge be for cutting them all up into similar one-foot lengths?"

It is curious that they could not at once agree as to the fair price for the job. What does the reader think the charge ought to be?

~5~
DIGGING A DITCH

Here is a curious question that is more perplexing than it looks at first sight. Abraham, an infirm old man, undertook to dig a ditch for 30 dollars. He engaged Benjamin, an able-bodied fellow, to assist him and share the money fairly according to their capacities. Abraham could dig as fast as Benjamin could shovel out the dirt, and Benjamin could dig four times as fast as Abraham could do the shovelling. How should they divide the money? Of course, we must assume their relative abilities for work to be the same in digging or shovelling.

~6~
NAME THEIR WIVES

A man left a legacy of $1000 to three relatives and their wives. The wives received together $396. Jane received $10 more than

Catherine, and Mary received $10 more than Jane. John Smith was given just as much as his wife, Henry Snooks got half as much again as his wife, and Tom Crowe received twice as much as his wife. What was the Christian name of each man's wife?

~7~
MARKET TRANSACTIONS

A farmer goes to market and buys a hundred animals at a total cost of $2000. The price of cows being $100 each, sheep $20 each, and rabbits $1. each, how many of each kind does he buy? Most people will solve this, if they succeed at all, by more or less laborious trial, but there are several direct ways of getting the solution.

AGE AND KINSHIP PUZZLES

~8~
THEIR AGES

If you add the square of Tom's age to the age of Mary, the sum is 62; but if you add the square of Mary's age to the age of Tom, the result is 176. Can you say what are the ages of Tom and Mary?

~9~
MRS. WILSON'S FAMILY

Mrs. Wilson had three children, Edgar, James, and John. Their combined ages were half of hers. Five years later, during which time Ethel was born, Mrs. Wilson's age equalled the total of all her children's ages. Ten years more have now passed, Daisy appearing during that interval. At the latter event Edgar was as old as John and Ethel together. The combined ages of all the children are now double Mrs.Wilson's age, which is, in fact, only equal to that of Edgar and James together. Edgar's age also equals that of the two daughters. Can you find all their ages?

~10~
DE MORGAN AND ANOTHER

Augustus de Morgan, the mathematician, who died in 1871, used to boast that he was x years old in the year x^2. My living friend, Jasper Jenkins, wishing to improve on this, tells me he was a^2+b^2 in a^4+b^4; that he was $2m$ in the year $2m^2$; and that he was $3n$ years old in the year $3n^4$. Can you give the years in which De Morgan and Jenkins were respectively born?

~11~
"SIMPLE" ARITHMETIC

When visiting a psychiatric institution, I asked two patients to give me their ages. They did so, and then, to test their arithmetical powers, I asked them to add the two ages together. One gave me 44 as the answer, and the other gave 1280. I immediately saw that the first had subtracted one age from the other, while the second person had multiplied them together. What were their ages?

CLOCK PUZZLES

~12~
WHAT IS THE TIME?

At what time are the two hands of a clock so situated that, reckoning as minute points past XII one is exactly the square of the distance of the other?

~13~
THE FIRST-BORN'S LEGACY

Mrs. Goodheart gave birth to twins. The clock showed clearly that Tommy was born about an hour later than Freddy. Mr. Goodheart, who died a few months earlier, had made a will leaving $12600, and had taken the precaution to provide for the possibility of there being twins. In such a case the money was to be divided in the following proportions: two-thirds to the widow, one-fifth to the first-born, one-tenth to the other twin, and one-twelfth to his brother. Now, what is the exact amount that should be settled on Freddy?

LOCOMOTION AND SPEED PUZZLES

~14~
HILL CLIMBING

Weary Willie went up a certain hill at the rate of one and a half miles per hour and came down at the rate of four and a half miles per hour, so that it took him just six hours to make the double journey. Now, how far was it to the top of the hill?

~15~
TIMING THE MOTOR-CAR

"I was walking along the road at three and a half miles an hour," said Mr. Pipkins, "when the motor-car dashed past me and only missed me by a few inches."

"Do you know at what speed it was going?" asked his friend.

"Well, from the moment it passed me to its disappearance round a corner I took twenty-seven steps, and walking on reached that corner with one hundred and thirty-five steps more."

"Then, assuming that you walked, and the car ran, each at a uniform rate, we can easily work out the speed."

~16~
THE STAIRCASE RACE

This is a rough sketch of the finish of a race up a staircase in which three men took part. Ackworth, who is leading, went up three risers at a time, as arranged; Barnden, the second man, went four risers at a time, and Croft, who is last, went five at a time.

Undoubtedly Ackworth wins. But the point is, how many risers are there in the stairs, counting the top landing as a riser?

I have only shown the top of the stairs. There may be scores, or hundreds, of risers below the line. It was not necessary to draw them, as I only wanted to show the finish. But it is possible to tell from the evidence the fewest possible risers in that staircase. Can you do it?

~17~
A WALKING PUZZLE

A man set out at noon to walk from Appleminster to Boneyham, and a friend of his started at two p.m. on the same day to walk from Boneyham to Appleminster. They met on the road at five minutes past four o'clock and each man reached his destination at exactly the same time. Can you say at what time they both arrived?

~18~
RIDING IN THE WIND

A man on a bicycle rode a mile in 3 minutes with the wind at his back, but it took him 4 minutes to return against the wind. How long would it take him to ride a mile if there was no wind?

Some will say that the average of 3 and 4 is 3½, and it would take him 3½ minutes. That answer is entirely wrong.

~19~
THE MOVING STAIRWAY

On one of the moving stairways on the London Tube Railway I find that if I walk down twenty-six steps I require thirty seconds to get to the bottom, but if I make thirty-four steps I require only eighteen seconds to reach the bottom. What is the height of the stairway in steps? The time is measured from the moment the top step begins to descend to the time I step off the last step at the bottom on to the level platform.

~20~
SHARING A BICYCLE

Two brothers had to go a journey and arrive at the same time. They had only a single bicycle, which they rode in turns, each rider leaving it in the hedge when he dismounted for the one walking behind to pick up, and walking ahead himself, to be again overtaken. What was their best way of arranging their distances? As their walking and riding speeds were the same, it is extremely easy. Simply divide the route into any *even* number of equal stages and drop the bicycle at every stage, using the cyclometer. Each man would then walk half-way and ride half-way.

But here is a case that will require a little more thought. Anderson and Brown have to go twenty miles and arrive at exactly the same time. They have only one bicycle. Anderson can only walk four miles an hour, while Brown can walk five miles an hour, but Anderson can ride ten miles an hour to Brown's eight miles an hour. How are they to arrange the journey? Each man always either walks or rides at the speeds mentioned, without any rests.

~21~
MORE BICYCLING

Referring to the last puzzle, let us now consider the case where a third rider has to share the same bicycle. As a matter of fact, I understand that Anderson and Brown have taken a man named

Carter into partnership, and the position to-day is this: Anderson, Brown, and Carter walk respectively four, five, and three miles per hour, and ride respectively ten, eight, and twelve miles per hour. How are they to use that single bicycle so that all shall complete the twenty miles' journey at the same time?

~22~
A Side-Car Problem

Atkins, Baldwin, and Clarke had to go a journey of fifty-two miles across country. Atkins had a motor-bicycle with side-car for one passenger. How was he to take one of his companions a certain distance, drop him on the road to walk the remainder of the way, and return to pick up the second friend, who, starting at the same time, was already walking on the road, so that they should all arrive at their destination at exactly the same time? The motor-bicycle could do twenty miles an hour, Baldwin could walk five miles an hour, and Clarke could walk four miles an hour. Of course, each went at his proper speed throughout and there was no waiting. I might have complicated the problem by giving more passengers, but I have purposely made it easy, and all the distances are an exact number of miles—without fractions.

~23~
The Despatch-Rider

If an army forty miles long advances forty miles while a despatch-rider gallops from the rear to the front, delivers a despatch to the commanding general, and returns to the rear, how far has he to travel?

~24~
The Two Trains

Two railway trains, one four hundred feet long and the other two hundred feet long, ran on parallel rails. It was found that when they went in opposite directions they passed each other in five seconds, but when they ran in the same direction the faster train would pass the other in fifteen seconds. Now, a curious passenger worked out from these facts the rate per hour at which each train ran. Can the reader discover the correct answer? Of course, each train ran with a uniform velocity.

~25~
THE DAMAGED ENGINE

We were going by train from Anglechester to Clinkerton, and an hour after starting some accident happened to the engine.

We had to continue the journey at three-fifths of the former speed, and it made us two hours late at Clinkerton, and the driver said that if only the accident had happened fifty miles farther on the train would have arrived forty minutes sooner. Can you tell from that statement just how far it is from Anglechester to Clinkerton?

~26~
THE PUZZLE OF THE RUNNERS

Two men ran a race round a circular course, going in opposite directions. Brown was the best runner and gave Tompkins a start of one-eighth of the distance. But Brown, with a contempt for his opponent, took things too easily at the beginning, and when he had run one-sixth of his distance he met Tompkins, and saw that his chance of winning the race was very small. How much faster than he went before must Brown now run in order to tie with his competitor? The puzzle is quite easy when once you have grasped its simple conditions.

~27~
THE TWO SHIPS

A correspondent asks the following question. Two ships sail from one port to another—two hundred nautical miles—and return. The *Mary Jane* travels outwards at twelve miles an hour and returns at eight miles an hour, thus taking forty-one and two-third hours for the double journey. The *Elizabeth Ann* travels both ways at ten miles an hour, taking forty hours on the double journey. Now, seeing that both ships travel at the average speed of ten miles per hour, why does the *Mary Jane* take longer than the *Elizabeth Ann*? Perhaps the reader could explain this little paradox.

~28~
FIND THE DISTANCE

A man named Jones set out to walk from A— to B—, and on the road he met his friend Kenward, ten miles from A—, who had left B— at exactly the same time. Jones executed his commission at B— and, without delay, set out on his return journey, while Kenward as promptly returned from A— to B—. They met twelve miles from B—. Of course, each walked at a uniform rate throughout. Now, how far is A— from B— ?

I will show the reader a simple rule by which the distance may be found by anyone in a few seconds without the use of a pencil. In fact, it is quite absurdly easy—when you know how to do it.

~29~
THE MAN AND THE DOG

"Yes; when I take my dog for a walk," said a mathematical friend, "he frequently supplies me with some interesting puzzle to solve. One day, for example, he waited, as I left the door, to see which way I should go, and when I started he raced along to the end of the road, immediately returning to me; again racing to the end of the road and again returning. He did this four times in all, at a uniform speed, and then ran at my side the remaining distance, which according to my paces measured 27 yards. I afterwards measured the distance from my door to the end of the road and found it to be 625 feet. Now, if I walk 4 miles per hour, what is the speed of my dog when racing to and fro?"

~30~
BAXTER'S DOG

This is an interesting companion to the "Man and Dog" puzzle. Anderson set off from a hotel at San Remo at nine o'clock and had been walking an hour when Baxter went after him along the same road. Baxter's dog started at the same time as his master and ran uniformly forwards and backwards between him and Anderson until the two men were together. Anderson's speed is two, Baxter's four, and the dog's ten miles an hour. How far had the dog run when Baxter overtook Anderson? My correspondent in Italy who sends me this is an exact man, and he says, "Neglect length of dog and time spent in turning." I will merely add, neglect also the dog's name and the day of the month.

~31~
RAILWAS SHUNTING

How are the two trains in our illustration to pass one another, and proceed with their engines in front? The small side-track is only large enough to hold one engine or one carriage at a time, and no tricks, such as ropes and flying-switches, are allowed. Every reversal—that is, change of direction—of an engine is counted as a move in the solution. What is the smallest number of moves necessary?

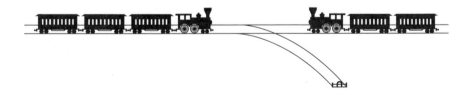

~32~
EXPLORING THE DESERT

Nine travellers, each possessing a motor-car, meet on the eastern edge of a desert. They wish to explore the interior, always going due west. Each car can travel forty miles on the contents of the engine tank, which holds a gallon of petrol, and each can carry nine extra gallon tins of petrol and no more. Unopened tins can alone be transferred from car to car. What is the greatest distance at which they can enter the desert without making any depots of petrol for the return journey?

GEOMETRICAL PROBLEMS

DISSECTION PUZZLES

~33~
DISSECTING THE MOON

In how large a number of pieces can this crescent moon be cut with five straight cuts of the knife? The pieces may not be piled or shifted after a cut.

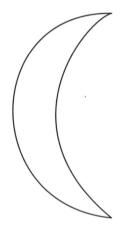

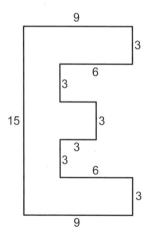

~34~
DISSECTING THE LETTER E

Can you cut this letter E into only five pieces so that they will fit together to form a perfect square? I have given all the measurements in inches so that there should be no doubt as to the correct proportions of the letter. In this case you are not allowed to turn over any piece.

~35~
A NEW CUTTING-OUT PUZZLE

Cut the figure into four pieces that will fit together and form a square.

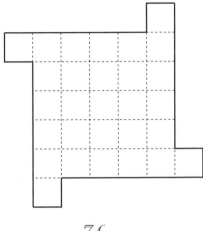

~36~
THE PIRATES' FLAG

Here is a flag taken from a band of pirates on the high seas. The twelve stripes represented the number of men in the band, and when a new man was admitted or dropped out a new stripe was added or one removed, as the case might be. Can you discover how the flag should be cut into as few pieces as possible so that they may be put together again and show only ten stripes? No part of the material may be wasted, and the flag must retain its oblong shape.

~37~
THE MUTILATED CROSS

Here is a symmetrical Greek Cross from which has been cut a square piece exactly equal to one of the arms of the cross. The puzzle is to cut what remains into four pieces that will fit together and form a square. This is a pleasing but particularly easy cutting-out puzzle.

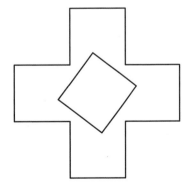

GEOMETRICAL PUZZLES

~38~
THE SIX SUBMARINES

Readers may remember a puzzle, to place five pennies so that every penny shall touch every other penny, that is given in my book, *Amusements in Mathematics*, and a correspondent has suggested that as many as six coins can be placed under the conditions if we arrange them as shown in the diagram below—that is, with A, B and C in the form of a triangle, and D, E, and F respectively on the top of A, B, and C. If we take a section of the coins at X Y (see the lower diagram), he held that E and C and also B and F meet at a "mathematical point," and are therefore in contact. But he was wrong, for if E touches C a barrier is set up between B and F. If B touches F, then E cannot touch C. It is a subtle fallacy that I know will interest my readers. When we say that a number of things meet at a point (like the spokes of a wheel) only three can be in contact (each with each) on the same plane.

This has led me to propound a new "touching" problem. If five submarines, sunk on the same day, all went down at the same spot where another had previously been sunk, how might they all lie at rest so that every one of the six U-boats should touch every other one? To simplify we will say, place six ordinary wooden matches so that every match shall touch every other match. No bending or breaking allowed.

~39~
ECONOMY IN STRING

Owing to the scarcity of string a lady found herself in this dilemma. In making up a parcel for her son, a prisoner in Germany, she was limited to using twelve feet of string, exclusive of knots, which passed round the parcel once lengthways and twice round its girth, as shown in the illustration. What was the largest rectangular parcel that she could make up, subject to these conditions?

MEASURING, WEIGHING, AND PACKING PUZZLES

~40~
A PROHIBITION POSER

Let us now take another step and look at those cases where we are still allowed any amount of waste, though the liquid is now limited to a stated quantity.

The American Prohibition authorities discovered a full barrel of beer, and were about to destroy the liquor by letting it run down a drain when the owner pointed to two vessels standing by and begged to be allowed to retain in them a small quantity for the immediate consumption of his household. One vessel was a 7-quart and the other a 5-quart measure. The officer was a wag, and, believing it to be impossible, said that if the man could measure an exact quart into each vessel (without any pouring back into the barrel) he might do so. How was it to be done in the fewest possible transactions without any marking or other tricks? Perhaps I should state that an American barrel of beer contains exactly 120 quarts.

~41~
PROHIBITION AGAIN

Let us now try to discover the fewest possible manipulations under the same conditions as in the last puzzle, except that we may now pour back into the barrel.

~42~
MONKEY AND PULLEY

Here is a funny tangle. It is a mixture of Lewis Carroll's "Monkey and Pulley," Loyd's "How old was Mary?" and some other trifles. But it is quite easy if you have a pretty clear head.

A rope is passed over a pulley. It has a weight at one end and a monkey at the other. There is the same length of rope on either side and equilibrium is maintained. The rope weighs four ounces per foot. The age of the monkey and the age of the monkey's mother together total four years. The weight of the monkey is as many pounds as the monkey's mother is years old. The monkey's mother is twice as old as the monkey was when the monkey's mother was half as old as the monkey will be when the monkey is three times as old as the monkey's mother was when the monkey's mother was three times as old as the monkey. The weight of the rope and the weight at the end was half as much again as the difference in weight between the weight of the weight and the weight and the weight of the monkey. Now, what was the length of the rope?

~43~
WEIGHING THE BABY

"I saw a funny incident at the railway station last summer," said a friend. "There was a little family group in front of the automatic weighing machine, that registered up to 200 lb, and they were engaged in the apparently difficult task of weighing the baby. Whenever they attempted to put the baby alone on the machine she always yelled and rolled off, while the father was holding off the dog, who always insisted on being included in the operations. At last the man, with the baby and Fido, were on the machine together, and I took this snapshot of them with my camera."

He produced a photograph, from which I have simply copied the dial, as that is all we need.

"Then the man turned to his wife and said, 'It seems to me, my dear, that baby and I together weigh 162 lb. more than the dog, while the dog weighs 70 per cent less than the baby. We must try to work it out at home.' I also amused myself by working it out from those figures. What do you suppose was the actual weight of that dear infant?"

CROSSING RIVER PROBLEMS

~44~

CROSSING THE FERRY

Six persons, all related, have to cross a river in a small boat that will only hold two. Mr. Webster, who had to plan the little affair, had quarrelled with his father-in-law and his son, and, I am sorry to say, Mrs. Webster was not on speaking terms with her own mother or her daughter-in-law, In fact, the relations were so strained that it was not safe to permit any of the belligerents to pass over together or to remain together on the same side of the river. And to prevent further discord, no man was to be left with two women or two men with three women. How are they to perform the feat in the fewest possible crossings? No tricks, such as making use of a rope or current, or swimming across, are allowed.

~45~
MISSIONARIES AND CANNIBALS

There is a strange story of three missionaries and three cannibals, who had to cross a river in a small boat that would only carry two men at a time. Being acquainted with the peculiar appetites of the cannibals, the missionaries could never allow their companions to be in a majority on either side of the river. Only one of the missionaries and one of the cannibals could row the boat. How did they manage to get across?

UNCLASSIFIED PROBLEMS

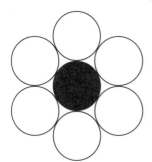

~46~
THE SIX PENNIES

Lay six pennies on the table, and then arrange them as shown by the six white circles in the illustration, so that if a seventh penny (the black circle) were produced it could be dropped in the centre and exactly touch each of the six. It is required to get it exact, without any dependence on the eye. In this case you are not allowed to lift any penny off the table—otherwise there would be no puzzle at all—nor can any measuring or marking be employed. You require only the six pennies.

~47~
AN INGENIOUS MATCH PUZZLE

Place six matches as shown, and then shift one match without touching the others so that the new arrangement shall represent an arithmetical fraction equal to 1. The match forming the horizontal fraction bar must not be the one moved.

~48~
FIFTY-SEVEN TO NOTHING

After the last puzzle, this one should be easy.

It will be seen that we have arranged six cigarettes so as to represent the number 57. The puzzle is to remove any two of them you like (without disturbing any of the others) and so replace them as to represent 0, or nothing. Remember that you can only shift two cigarettes. There are two entirely different solutions. Can you find one or both?

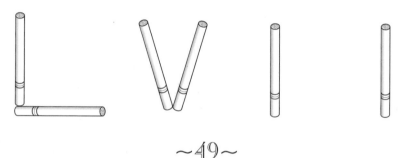

~49~
THE FIVE SQUARES

Here is a new little match puzzle that will perplex a good many readers, though they will smile when they see the answer. It will be seen that the twelve matches are so arranged that they form four squares. Can you rearrange the same number of matches (all lying flat on the table) so that they enclose five squares? Every square must be entirely "empty" or the illustration itself will show five squares, if we are allowed to count the large square forming the boundary. No duplicated match or loose ends are allowed.

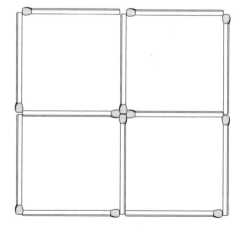

~50~
THE FLY'S TOUR

I had a ribbon of paper, divided into squares on each side, as shown in the illustration. I joined the two ends together to make a ring, which I threw on the table. Later I noticed that a fly pitched on the ring and walked in a line over every one of the squares on both sides, returning to the point from which it started, *without ever passing over the edge of the paper!* Its course passed through the centres of the squares all the time. How was this possible?

SOLUTIONS

~1~
DOLLARS AND CENTS

The man must have entered the store with 99.98 dollars in his pocket.

~2~
UNREWARDED LABOUR

Weary Willie must have worked 16⅔ days and idled 13⅓ days. Thus the former time, at $24 a day, amounts to exactly the same as the latter at $30 a day, that is $400.

~3~
THE PERPLEXED BANKER

The contents of the ten bags should be as follows: 1, 2, 4, 8, 16, 32, 64, 128, 256, 489. The first nine numbers are in geometrical progression, and their sum, deducted from 1000, gives the contents of the tenth bag.

~4~
SAWING LOGS

In the first case the charge was $10 a cord for short logs. Four cords of long logs would equal in number of logs two cords of short logs, but every long log would need five cuts to two cuts in the case of short logs. Therefore, the charge should be in the proportion of 5 to 4, or $12.50 a cord, as compared with $10 a cord, and four cords at $12.50 would be $50, the correct charge.

~5~
DIGGING A DITCH

A. should receive one-third of thirty dollars ($10), and B. two-thirds ($20). Say B. can dig all in 2 hours and shovel all in 4 hours; then A. can dig all in 4 hours and shovel all in 8 hours. That is, their ratio of digging is as 2 to 4 and their ratio of shovelling as 4 to 8 (the same ratio), and A. can dig in the same time that B. can shovel (4 hours), while B. can dig in a quarter of the time that A. can shovel. Any other figures will do that fill these conditions and give two similar ratios for their working ability. Therefore, A. takes one-third and B. twice as much—two-thirds.

~6~
NAME THEIR WIVES

As it is evident that Catherine, Jane, and Mary received respectively $122, $132, and $142, making together the $396 left to the three wives, if John Smith receives as much as his wife Catherine, $122; Henry Snooks half as much again as his wife Jane, $198; and Tom Crowe twice as much as his wife Mary, $284, we have correctly paired these married couples and exactly accounted for the $1000.

~7~
MARKET TRANSACTIONS

The man bought 19 cows for $1900, 1 sheep for $20, and 80 rabbits for $80, making together 100 animals at a cost of $2000.

A purely arithmetical solution is not difficult by a method of averages, the average cost per animal being the same as the cost of a sheep.

By algebra we proceed as follows:

$$
\begin{array}{rl}
100x + 20y + z = & 2000 \\
x + y + z = & 100 \\
\hline
99x + 19y = & 1900
\end{array}
$$

by subtraction. We have therefore to solve this indeterminate equation, when we find that the only answer is x=19, y=1. Then, to make up the 100 animals, z must=80.

~8~
THEIR AGES
Tom's age was seven years and Mary's thirteen years.

~9~
MRS. WILSON'S FAMILY
The ages must have been as follows: Mrs. Wilson, 39; Edgar, 21; James, 18; John, 18; Ethel, 12; Daisy, 9. It is clear that James and John were twins.

~10~
DE MORGAN AND ANOTHER
De Morgan was born in 1806. When he was 43, the year was the square of his age—1849. Jenkins was born in 1860. He was 5^2+6^2 (61) in the year 5^4+6^4 (1921). Also he was 2x31 (62) in the year $2x31^2$ (1922). Again, he was 3x5 (15) in the year $3x5^4$ (1875).

~11~
"SIMPLE" ARITHMETIC
Their ages were respectively 64 and 20.

~12~
WHAT IS THE TIME?
The time is 6¾ minutes past IX, when the hour-hand is 45⁹/₁₆ minutes past XII. Then 45⁹/₁₆ is the square of 6¾. If we allow fractions *less* than a minute point then there is also the solution, five seconds (one-twelfth of a minute) past XII o'clock.

~13~
THE FIRST-BORN'S LEGACY

The fractions $\frac{2}{3}$, $\frac{1}{5}$, $\frac{1}{10}$, $\frac{1}{12}$, equal $\frac{40}{60}$, $\frac{12}{60}$, $\frac{6}{60}$, $\frac{5}{60}$, which together make $\frac{63}{60}$ which is greater than unity, but the legacies were to be in the *"proportions"* of those fractions. Therefore, the widow receives $\frac{40}{63}$=$8000, the first-born $\frac{12}{63}$=$2400, the second-born $\frac{6}{63}$=$1200, and the brother $\frac{5}{63}$=$1000. But the sting is in the tail, and the question is indeterminate until we learn just *when* the twins were born. Tommy was actually born just before 2 a.m. on 21st September, 1924, immediately after which time the clocks were set back an hour, summer time being ended, and Freddy was born a little after 1 a.m. "by the clock." So we have the curious paradox that the first-born was born later than the second-born! Freddy therefore only receives $1200.

~14~
HILL CLIMBING

It must have been $6\frac{3}{4}$ miles to the top of the hill. He would go up in $4\frac{1}{2}$ hours and descend in $1\frac{1}{2}$ hours.

~15~
TIMING THE MOTOR-CAR

As the man can walk 27 steps while the car goes 162, the car is clearly going six times as fast as the man. The man walks $3\frac{1}{2}$ miles an hour: therefore the car was going at 21 miles an hour.

~16~
THE STAIRCASE RACE

If the staircase were such that each man would reach the top in a certain number of full leaps, without taking a reduced number at his last leap, the smallest possible number of risers would, of course, be 60 (that is, 3x4x5). But the sketch showed us that A. taking three risers at a leap, has one odd step at the end; B. taking four at a leap, will have three only at the end; and C. taking five at a leap, will have four only at the finish. Therefore, we have to find the smallest number that, when divided by 3, leaves a remainder 1, when divided by 4 leaves 3, and when divided by 5 leaves a remainder 4. This number is 19. So there were 19 risers in all, only four being left out in the sketch.

~17~
A WALKING PUZZLE

It will be found (and it is the key to the solution) that the man from B. can walk 7 miles while the man from A. can walk 5 miles. Say the distance between the towns is 24 miles, then the point of meeting would be 14 miles from A. and the man from A. walked $3\frac{3}{7}$ miles per hour, while the man from B. walked $4\frac{4}{5}$ miles per hour. They both arrived at 7 p.m. exactly.

~18~
RIDING IN THE WIND

He could ride one mile in $3\frac{3}{7}$ minutes, or $\frac{7}{24}$ mile per minute. The wind would help or retard him to the extent of $\frac{1}{24}$ mile per minute. Therefore, with the wind he could ride $\frac{8}{24}$ mile per minute and against the wind $\frac{6}{24}$ mile per minute; so that is 1 mile in 3 minutes, or 4 minutes respectively, as stated.

~19~
THE MOVING STAIRWAY

If I walk 26 steps I require 30 seconds, and if I walk 34 steps I require only 18 seconds. Multiply 30 by 34 and 26 by 18 and we get 1020 and 468, the difference between which is 552. Divide this by the difference between 30 and 18 (that is, by 12) and the answer is 46, the number of steps in the stairway, which descends at the rate of 1 step in $1\frac{1}{2}$ seconds. The speed at which I walk on the stairs does not affect the question, as the step from which I alight will reach the bottom at a given moment, whatever I do in the meantime.

~20~
Sharing a Bicycle

Let Anderson ride $11\frac{1}{9}$ miles, drop the bicycle, and walk the rest of the way. Brown will walk until he picks up the bicycle, and then rides to their destination, getting there at exactly the same time as Anderson. The journey takes them 3 hours 20 minutes. Or you can divide the 20 miles into nine stages of $2\frac{2}{9}$ miles each, and drop the machine at every stage, only you must make Anderson ride at the start. Anderson will then ride each of his five stages in $\frac{2}{9}$ hour and walk each of his four stages in $\frac{5}{9}$ hour, making his total time $3\frac{1}{3}$ hours. Brown will ride each of his four stages in $\frac{5}{18}$ hour and walk each of his five stages in $\frac{4}{9}$ hour, making his total time also $3\frac{1}{3}$ hours. The distances that Anderson and Brown ride respectively must be in the proportion of 5 to 4; the distances they walk in the proportion of 4 to 5.

~21~
More Bicycling

A. rides $7\frac{11}{27}$ miles, B. rides $1\frac{13}{27}$ miles, and C. rides $11\frac{3}{27}$ miles, making the twenty miles in all. They may ride in any order, only each man should complete his ride in one mount and the second rider must always walk both before and after riding. They will each take $3\frac{8}{9}$ hours on the journey, and therefore will all arrive together.

~22~
A Side-Car Problem

Atkins takes Clarke 40 miles in his car and leaves him to walk the remaining 12 miles. He then rides back and picks up Baldwin at a point 16 miles from the start and takes him to their destination. All three arrive in exactly 5 hours. Or Atkins might take Baldwin 36 miles and return for Clarke, who will have walked his 12 miles. The side-car goes 100 miles in all, with no passenger for 24 miles.

~23~
THE DESPATCH-RIDER

The answer is the square root of twice the square of 40, added to 40. This is 96.568 miles, or, roughly, $96\frac{1}{2}$ miles.

~24~
THE TWO TRAINS

In 5 seconds both trains (together) go 600 feet, or $81\frac{9}{11}$ miles per hour. In 15 seconds the faster train gains 600 feet, or $27\frac{3}{11}$ miles per hour. From this we get $54\frac{6}{11}$ miles per hour as the rate of the faster train; and it is clear that $27\frac{3}{11}$ miles per hour is the rate of the other.

~25~
THE DAMAGED ENGINE

The distance from Anglechester to Clinkerton must be 200 miles. The train went 50 miles at 50 m.p.h. and 150 miles at 30 m.p.h. If the accident had occured 50 miles farther on, it would have gone 100 miles at 50 m.p.h. and 100 miles at 30 m.p.h.

~26~
THE PUZZLE OF THE RUNNERS

While Brown has only run $\frac{1}{6}$ or $\frac{4}{24}$ of the course, Tompkins has run the remainder $\frac{5}{6}$, less $\frac{1}{8}$, or $\frac{17}{24}$. Therefore Tompkins's pace is $\frac{17}{4}$ times that of Brown. Brown has now $\frac{5}{6}$ of the course to run, whereas Tompkins has only $\frac{1}{6}$. Therefore Brown must go five times as fast as Tompkins, or increase his own speed to five times $\frac{17}{4}$, that is $\frac{85}{4}$ times as fast as he went at first. But the question was not how many times as fast, but "how much faster," and $\frac{85}{4}$ times as fast is equal to $\frac{81}{4}$ times faster than Brown's original speed. The correct answer is therefore $20\frac{1}{4}$ times faster, though in practice probably impossible.

~27~
THE TWO SHIPS

The error lies in assuming that the average speeds are equal. They are not. The first ship does a mile in a twelfth of an hour outwards and in an eighth of an hour homewards. Half of the sum of these fractions is five forty-eighths. Therefore the ship's average speed for the four hundred miles is a mile in five forty-eighths of an hour. The average speed of the second ship is a mile in one-tenth of an hour.

~28~
FIND THE DISTANCE

The distance between the two places must have been 18 miles. The meeting-points were 10 miles from A— and 12 miles from B—. Simply multiply 10 (the first distance) by 3 and deduct the second distance, 12. Could anything be simpler? Try other distances for the meeting-points (taking care that the first meeting distance is more than two-thirds of the second) and you will find the little rule will always work.

~29~
THE MAN AND THE DOG

The dog's speed was 16 miles per hour. The following facts will give the reader clues to the general solution. The distance remaining to be walked side by side with the dog was 81 feet, the fourth power of 3 (for the dog returned four times), and the distance to the end of the road was 625 feet, the fourth power of 5. Then the difference between the speeds (in miles per hour) of man and dog (that is, 12) and the sum of the speeds (20) must be in the same ratio, 3 to 5, as is the case.

~30~
BAXTER'S DOG

It is obvious that Baxter will overtake Anderson in one hour, for each will be four miles from the hotel in the same direction. Then, as the dog has been running uniformly at ten miles an hour during that hour, he must have run ten miles! When a friend put this problem before a French professor of mathematics, he exclaimed: *"Mon Dieu, quelle serie!"* quite overlooking the simple manner of solution.

~31~
RAILWAY SHUNTING

Make a rough sketch like our diagram and use five counters marked X, L, R, A, and B. The engines are L and R, and the two cars on the right A and B. The three cars on the left are never separated, so we call them X. The side-track is marked S. Now, play as follows: R to left, R to S, X L to right, R to left, X L A to left, L takes A to S, L to left,

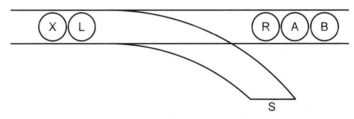

X L to right, R to A, R A to left, X L B to left, L takes B to S, L to left, L X right away, R A to B, R A B right away. Fourteen moves, because the first and third moves (R to left and X L to right) do not involve a change of direction. It cannot be done in fewer moves.

~32~
EXPLORING THE DESERT

The nine men, A, B, C, D, E, F, G, H, J, all go 40 miles together on the 1 gall. in their engine tanks, when A transfers 1 gall. to each of the other eight and has 1 gall. left to return home. The eight go another 40 miles, when B transfers 1 gall. to each of the other seven and has 2 galls. to take him home. The seven go another 40 miles, when C transfers 1 gall. to each of the six others and returns home on the remaining 3 galls. The six go another 40 miles, when D gives each of five 1 gall. and returns home. The five go 40 miles, when E gives each of four 1 gall. and returns home. The four go another 40 miles, when F gives each of three 1 gall. and returns home. The three go 40 miles, when G gives each of two 1 gall. and returns home. The two go 40 miles, when H gives 1 gall. to J and returns home. Finally, the last man, J, goes another 40 miles and then has 9 galls. to take him home. Thus J has gone 360 miles out and home, the greatest distance in a straight line that could be reached under the conditions.

~33~
DISSECTING THE MOON

The illustration shows that the five cuts can be so cunningly made as to produce as many as twenty-one pieces.

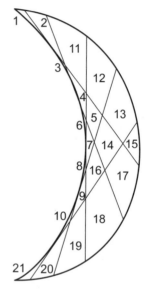

Calling the number of cuts *n*, then in the case of a circle the maximum number of pieces will be, $\frac{n^2+n}{2}+1$ but in the case of the crescent it will be $\frac{n^2+3n}{2}+1$.

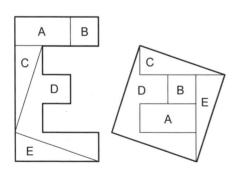

~34~
DISSECTING THE LETTER E

The illustration shows how to cut the letter into five pieces that will fit together to form a perfect square. It can be done in four pieces if you are allowed to turn pieces over. Readers may like to find for themselves the method.

~35~
A NEW CUTTING-OUT
PUZZLE

Make the cuts as shown in the illustration and fit the pieces into the places enclosed by the dotted lines.

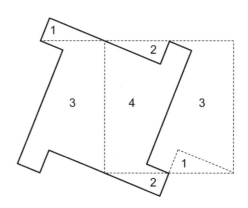

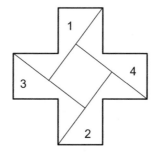

~36~
THE PIRATES' FLAG

The illustration will show that the flag need only be cut in two pieces—along the zigzag line. If the lower piece is then moved up one step we shall get a flag with the required ten stripes.

~37~
THE MUTILATED
CROSS

The illustration shows clearly how to cut the mutilated cross into four pieces to form a square. Just continue each side of the square until you strike a corner, and there you are!

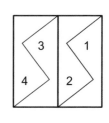

~38~
THE SIX SUBMARINES

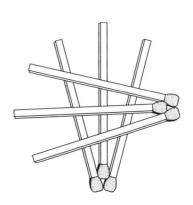

It will be seen from the illustration that this puzzle is absurdly easy— when you know how to do it! And yet I have not the slightest doubt that many readers found it a hard nut to crack. It will be seen that every match undoubtedly touches every other match.

~39~
ECONOMY IN STRING

The total length of string that passes along the length, breadth, or depth must in every case be the same to allow for the maximum dimensions—that is, 4 feet. When the reader is told this, or has found it for himself (and I think the point will be found interesting), the rest is exceedingly easy. For the string passes 2 times along length, 4 times along breadth, and 6 times along depth. Therefore 4 feet divided by 2, 4, and 6 will give us 2 feet, 1 foot, and ⅔ foot respectively for the length, breadth, and depth of the largest possible parcel.

The following general solution is by Mr. Alexander Fraser. Let the string pass a times along length x, b times along breadth y, and c times along depth z, and let length of string be m.

Then $ax+by+cz=m$. Find maximum value of xyz.

First find maximum area of xy.

~40~
A PROHIBITION POSER

First fill and waste the 7-quart measure 14 times and you will have thrown away 98 and leave 22 quarts in the barrel in 28 transactions. (Filling and emptying are 2 transactions.) Then, fill 7-qt.; fill 5-qt. from

7-qt., leaving 2 in 7-qt.; empty 5-qt.; transfer 2 from 7-qt. to 5-qt.; fill 7-qt.; fill up 5-qt. from 7-qt., leaving 4 in 7-qt.; empty 5-qt.; transfer 4 to 5-qt.; fill 7-qt.; fill up 5-qt. from 7-qt., leaving 6 in 7-qt.; empty 5-qt.; fill 5-qt. from 7-qt., leaving 1 in 7-qt.; empty 5-qt., leaving 1 in 7-qt.; draw off remaining 1-qt. from barrel into 5-qt., and the thing is done in 14 more transactions, making, with the 28 above, 42 transactions. Or you can start by wasting 104 and leaving 16 in barrel. These 16 can be dealt with in 10 transactions, and the 104 require 32 in the wasting (12 times 7 and 4 times 5 is the quickest way).

~41~
PROHIBITION AGAIN

Fill 7-qt.; fill 5-qt.; empty 108 quarts from barrel; empty 5-qt. into barrel; fill 5-qt. from 7-qt.; empty 5-qt. into barrel; pour 2 quarts from 7-qt. into 5-qt.; fill 7-qt. from barrel; fill up 5-qt. from 7-qt.; empty 5-qt. into barrel; pour 4 quarts from 7-qt. into 5-qt.; fill 7-qt. from barrel; fill up 5-qt. from 7-qt.; throw away contents of 5-qt.; fill 5-qt. from 7-qt.; throw away 5 quarts from 5-qt.; empty 1 quart from barrel into 5-qt. The feat is thus performed in 17 transactions—the fewest possible.

~42~
MONKEY AND PULLEY

We find the age of the monkey works out at 1½ years, and the age of the mother 2½ years, the monkey therefore weighing 2½ lb., and the weight the same. Then we soon discover that the rope weighed 1¼ lb., or 20 oz.; and, as a foot weighed 4 oz., the length of the rope was 5 feet.

~43~
WEIGHING THE BABY

It is important to notice that the man, baby, and dog weigh together 180 lb., as recorded on the dial in the illustration. Now, the difference between 180 and 162 is 18, which equals twice the weight of the dog, whose weight is 9 lb. Therefore the baby weighs 30 lb., since 30 less 70 per cent is 9.

~44~
CROSSING THE FERRY

The puzzle can be solved in as few as nine crossings, as follows: (1) Mr. and Mrs. Webster cross. (2) Mrs. Webster returns. (3) Mother and daughter-in-law cross. (4) Mr. Webster returns. (5) Father-in-law and son cross. (6) Daughter-in-law returns. (7) Mr. Webster and daughter-in-law cross. (8) Mr. Webster returns. (9) Mr. and Mrs. Webster cross.

~45~
MISSIONARIES AND CANNIBALS

Call the three missionaries M m m, and the three cannibals C c c, the capitals denoting the missionary and the cannibal who can row the boat. Then C c row across; C returns with the boat; C c row across; C returns; M m row across; M c return; M C row across; M c return; M m row across; C returns; C c row across; C returns; C c row across; and all have crossed the river within the conditions stated.

~46~
THE SIX PENNIES

First arrange the pennies as in Diagram A. Then carefully shift 6 and get position B. Next place 5 against 2 and 3 to get the position C. No. 3 can now be placed in the position indicated by the dotted circle.

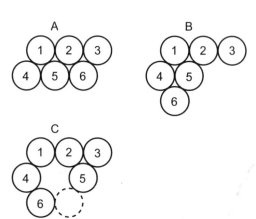

~47~
AN INGENIOUS MATCH PUZZLE

It will be seen that the second I in VII has been moved, so as to form the sign of square root. The square root of 1 is, of course, 1, so that the fractional expression itself represents 1.

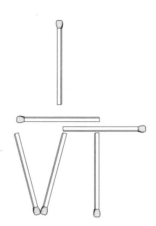

~48~
FIFTY-SEVEN TO NOTHING

Remove the two cigarettes forming the letter L in the original arrangement, and replace them in the way shown in our illustration. We have the square root of 1 minus 1 (that is 1 less 1), which clearly

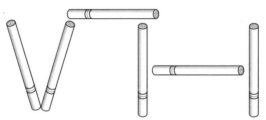

is 0. In the second case we can remove the same two cigarettes and, by placing one against the V and the other against the second I, form the word NIL, or nothing.

~49~
THE FIVE SQUARES

Place the twelve matches as in the diagram and five squares are enclosed. It is true that the one in the centre (indicated by the arrow) is very small, but no conditions were imposed as to dimensions.

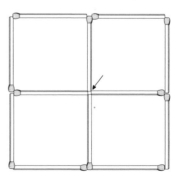

~50~
THE FLY'S TOUR

Before you join the ends give one end of the ribbon a half-turn, so that there is a twist in the ring. Then the fly can walk over all the squares without going over the edge, for we have the curious paradox of a piece of paper with only one side and one edge!

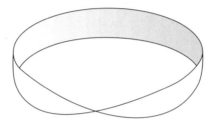

Note: In Mathematics this is called a Möbius strip.